TAKING PART

HELPING YOUNG CHILDREN TAKE PART IN A STATUTORY ASSESSMENT OF THEIR SPECIAL EDUCATIONAL NEEDS

by
Hannah Mortimer

A QEd Publication

Published in 2000

© Hannah Mortimer

ISBN 1 898873 14 3

Published by QEd, The Rom Building, Eastern Avenue, Lichfield, Staffs. WS13 6RN

Printed in the United Kingdom by Stowes (Stoke-on-Trent).

Introduction

There is a requirement that all pupils be involved in their own statutory assessment, and that their views are sought and taken into account. Sometimes, very young children may be unable to make their views known without additional help.

Recognising the importance of pupil participation, this booklet has been written so that you can talk through what will happen when a young child's special educational needs are being assessed. The book is written from a child's perspective and in such a way that children can read it themselves, or have it read to them by an adult. Similarly, children can be encouraged to fill in the spaces themselves or have them filled in by a helper. At the end of the book there are two pages which the child or helper can complete and be used as the child's contribution, or additional evidence, to his or her statutory assessment.

Any form of assessment can be a daunting and confusing process for young children. The book will help the child become interested in the assessment, explain what will happen, who the child will meet, and encourage the child to say what kind of help he or she wants. It also provides a framework to help the child see his or her own special educational needs.

The booklet describes you as the child's 'grown-up'. You may be the parent, a carer, a teacher, a psychologist or another professional working with the child. Use the booklet flexibly and adapt it to suit your child and your situation.

It is best suited for children up to 8 or 9 years of age who are able to understand a story.

Everybody is different — everyone is special

Everybody is different, nobody is the same. If you look around, you will see some children who don't see very well. They have to wear glasses in order to see. Other children might break out in a rash when they eat certain foods (this is called being allergic). Others cannot hear very well, or don't talk like everyone else. Some children are very short, or very tall, or very weak, or very strong. Some children take longer to learn things than others.

Think of your friends. Talk to your own grown-up about how each one is different.

Everybody is different, and each one is special.

....

Let's talk about you.

How are you different?

How are you special?

Talk to your grown-up about what <u>you</u> look like.

Look in the mirror together and help think of some words to describe yourself.

What I look like

Talk to your grown-up about the things that <u>you</u> like.

Things that make me happy.

My favourite toy

....

My favourite game

....

My favourite story or song

....

My favourite outing or activity

....

....

Things that make me especially happy

....

....

....

Talk to your grown-up about the things that frighten you or make you sad.

Things that worry me.

Write down

Things that make me sad
Things that make me worried
Things that make me cross
We all need someone to talk to. When I am sad I talk to ...

Talk to your grown-up about all the things you have learned to do at home, playgroup, nursery or at school.

Things I can do.

Write down

The things I have learned to do

The things I find difficult to do

Many of these things are **exactly** what other children your age will be doing. So you will be doing things no differently from other children, and often better.

So you see, even though you are special in some ways, there are things you can do the same or better than other children.

Write these or ask your grown-up to write some of them down

What are my 'special educational needs'?

Because you are special, there may be some things that you need more help with than other children. Perhaps you need special help to walk, or to speak, to hear, or to learn things.

Talk to your grown-up about what it is that makes you need special help. Find some words together that you can use to describe your 'special needs'.

My Special Educational Needs

Perhaps you have already been having some special help. Talk to your grown-up about the special people who help you now and what they do.

My Special Helpers

Some of your helpers think that you might need extra help as you grow older. Your grown-up will tell you who, and why.

My Special Helpers as I Grow Older

My Statutory Assessment

The next few weeks will be called your 'statutory assessment', and by completing this workbook you can help too.

What will happen first?

Your parents or carers, and the helpers who look after you, will be asked to write down all the things you have learned to do, the things you find it difficult to do, and the sort of help and teaching you are going to need.

You may know these helpers already, and you may get to know some new people.

If your grown-up knows, ask for the names of the helpers who will be part of your statutory assessment.

My parents or carers	
My doctor	
My educational psychologist	
My teacher	
My social worker (if I have one)	

Your **doctor** will be looking at how well your eyes can see and your ears can hear. Your grown-up will probably take you along to the clinic, and will stay with you. The doctor may listen to your heart beating and your chest breathing. You might have a light shone in your ears and eyes. None of this hurts.

Your grown-up will also tell the doctor about any illnesses you have had, and how you have changed since you were a baby. These changes are called your 'development'.

You will also meet an **educational psychologist**. These helpers are teachers who have been specially trained to understand how children develop, how they behave, and how they learn. The psychologist may visit you and your grown-up at home, or, if you go to school or nursery, may meet you there.

You may play together and you may be given some puzzles to do. You may be able to show off some of your work. The psychologist is interested in how you play, how you talk, and how you think and learn. You will probably enjoy your time with the psychologist.

You will also meet a **teacher**. If you go to school or nursery, this will be the teacher you already know. If you are still at home, then a teacher may come to visit you and your grown-up. The teacher will bring toys and activities with him or her, and most children enjoy this time together very much. You might like to show off your favourite toys and games.

What happens then?

Once all your helpers have written down what you can do, and what special help you need, they will send this to an office called the 'Education Authority'.

The people who work in the Education Authority will discuss this and may decide to do something special to help you. This will be written down for your family on a piece of paper called a 'statement'. This makes sure you get the help you need.

Even if you don't have a 'statement', your carers and teachers should go on helping you in the same ways for as long as you need it.

What sort of help do children have?

Some children have extra help when they go to school. Perhaps there is an extra helper in the classroom to give them more time, help them move around, or help them to learn. Some children have some extra teaching. Some children need special ways of teaching.

Some children need special equipment like a hearing aid, a special computer, or a wheelchair.

Some children go to a different school where there are only a few children in a class and lots of extra help.

What sort of extra help do you have now, and what sort of extra help would you like?

Help I have now	Help I would like

Talk through with your grown-up the sort of help you might need in school. For some things you might need no help at all. But because of your 'special educational needs' you might need help for other things.

What help would you need?

to move around?
to manage your coat?
to go to the toilet?
to drink?
to talk clearly?
to hold a pencil?
to hear?
to see?
to make friends?
to play?
to learn at school?

How can you help with your statutory assessment?

There is a 'law' or rule which says that you should help with your statutory assessment. You are the most important person and your grown-ups and helpers will help you understand what is happening. They also need to ask you what sort of help **you** want.

Because you have worked with this book, your grown-ups and helpers can now help to copy your ideas into a letter telling the Education Authority what **you** think.

Your grown-up will send this for you, or give it to one of the other helpers taking part in your assessment.

You might like to add your name on the letter to show that you have talked all about it.

If you want to ask questions about the sort of help you can be given, any of the helpers can find out for you. Tell your grown-up if you want to talk to anyone special.

Look after this booklet so that you can show your school all the thinking and talking work you have done.

Young Child's Contribution to Statutory Assessment

My Name ....

My Birthday .... **My Age** ....

This form was written up by ....

who is my ....

This is how we describe my special educational needs	
These are the things I have learned to do	
These are the things I find difficult	
These are the things that make me happy	
These are the things that worry me	

Young Child's Contribution to Statutory Assessment — page 2

The Help I Need

This is the
special help I
have now

This is the kind
of help I will
need in the
future

I would need
special help
with these
things at school

I would like to
talk to this person
again about my
assessment and
help

This is my name

Date ....